AARON COPLAND

Appalachian Spring Suite

TRANSCRIBED FOR SOLO PIANO
by Bryan Stanley

BOOSEY & HAWKES

DISTRIBUTED BY

HAL•LEONARD®
CORPORATION
7777 W. BLUEMOUND RD. P.O. BOX 13819 MILWAUKEE, WI 53213

For all works contained herein:
Unauthorized copying, arranging, adapting, recording or public performance is an infringement of copyright.
Infringers are liable under the law.

www.boosey.com
www.halleonard.com

AARON COPLAND
(1900-1990)

Aaron Copland's name is, for many, synonymous with American music. It was his pioneering achievement to break free from Europe and create a concert music that is recognizably, characteristically American. At the same time, he was able to stamp his music with a compositional personality so vivid as to transcend stylistic boundaries, making every work—from the easily-grasped to the demanding—identifiable as his alone.

From his early studies in piano he proceeded, at age 17, to study harmony, counterpoint, and sonata form with Rubin Goldmark, whose staunchly conservative outlook inspired Copland to rebellious investigation of the music of Debussy, Ravel, Mussorgsky, and Scriabin. In 1920, he set out for Paris, modernism's home in the years between the wars. Among the many vital legacies of his stay in Paris were his association with his teacher and mentor Nadia Boulanger; a growing interest in popular idioms; and the insight that there was as yet no American counterpart to the national styles being created by composers from France, Russia, and Spain. He became determined to create, in his words, "a naturally American strain of so-called serious music."

Upon his return to America in 1924, his career was launched when Serge Koussevitzky, whom he had met in Paris, agreed to conduct the Boston Symphony Orchestra in Copland's Organ Symphony, with Boulanger as soloist. When performed in New York under Walter Damrosch, the dissonant, angular work created a sensation. But Copland saw a broader role for himself than mere iconoclast. He sought to further the cause of new music as a vital cultural force. He accomplished this not only by composing, but also by lecturing and writing on new music, and by organizing the groundbreaking Copland-Sessions concerts in New York, which brought many works of the European avant-garde to U.S. audiences for the first time.

As America entered first a Depression, and then a war, Copland began to share many of his fellow artists' commitment to capturing a wider audience and speaking to the concerns of the average citizen in those times of trouble. His intentions were fulfilled as works from *Billy the Kid* to *Lincoln Portrait* to the Pulitzer Prize-winning *Appalachian Spring* found both popular success and critical acclaim. His decision to "say it in the simplest possible terms" alienated some of his peers, who saw in it a repudiation of musical progress—theirs and his own. But many who had been drawn to Copland's music through his use of familiar melodies were in turn perplexed by his use, beginning in the mid-1950's, of an individualized 12-tone compositional technique. His orchestral works *Connotations* (1962) and *Inscape* (1967) stand as perhaps the definitive statements of his mature, "difficult" style.

Copland never ceased to be an emissary and advocate of new music. In 1951, he became the first American composer to hold the position of Norton Professor of Poetics at Harvard University; his lectures there were published as *Music and Imagination*. For 25 years he was a leading member of the faculty at the Berkshire Music Center (Tanglewood). Throughout his career, he nurtured the careers of others, including Leonard Bernstein, Carlos Chavez, Toru Takemitsu, and David Del Tredici. He took up conducting while in his fifties, becoming a persuasive interpreter of his own music; he continued to conduct in concerts, on the radio, and on television until he was 83.

Aaron Copland was one of the most honored cultural figures in the history of the United States. The Presidential Medal of Freedom, the Kennedy Center Award, the National Academy of Motion Picture Arts and Sciences "Oscar", and the Commander's Cross of the Order of Merit of the Federal Republic of Germany were only a few of the honors and awards he received. In addition, he was president of the American Academy of Arts and Letters; a fellow of the Royal Academy of Music and the Royal Society of Arts in England; helped found the American Composers Alliance; was an early and prominent member of the American Society of Composers, Authors, and Publishers; served as director or board member of the American Music Center, the Koussevitzky Foundation, the League of Composers, and other organizations; received honorary doctorates from over 40 colleges and universities. In 1982, The Aaron Copland School of Music was established in his honor at Queens College of the City University of New York.

APPALACHIAN SPRING

This note appeared in the scores of the original chamber ensemble suite for 13 instruments, and the suite for symphony orchestra:

Appalachian Spring was composed in 1943–44 as a ballet for Miss Martha Graham on a commission from the Elisabeth Sprague Coolidge Foundation. It was first performed by Miss Graham and her company at the Coolidge Festival in the Library of Congress, Washington, D.C., on October 30, 1944.

The action of the ballet concerns "a pioneer celebration in spring around a newly-built farmhouse in the Pennsylvania hills in the early part of the last century [1800s]. The bride-to-be and the young farmer-husband enact the emotions, joyful and apprehensive, their new domestic partnership invites. An Older neighbor suggests now and then the rocky confidence of experience. A revivalist and his followers remind the new householders of the strange and terrible aspects of human fate. At the end the couple is left quiet and strong in their new house."

In 1945 *Appalachian Spring* received the Pulitzer Prize for music, as well as the award of the Music Critics Circle of New York for the outstanding theatrical work of the season of 1944–45.

ABOUT THE SOLO PIANO TRANSCRIPTION

We have consulted the scores of the original version for 13 instrument chamber ensemble and the composer's 1945 suite for symphony orchestra. This solo piano transcription follows the musical form of the 1945 orchestral suite. All tempo indications and expressive markings have been retained, as have most articulations. Small, occasional adjustments have been made to create an idiomatic piano work. We refer the pianist to the study score of the orchestral suite for consideration of instrumental timbres.

Appalachian Spring Suite
(Ballet for Martha)

AARON COPLAND
Transcribed for piano solo
by Bryan Stanley

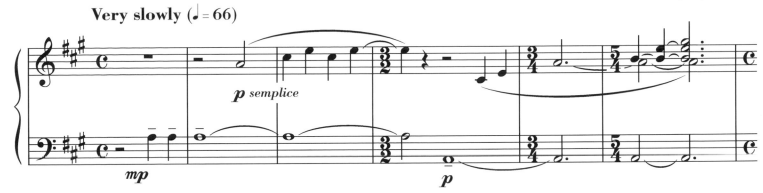

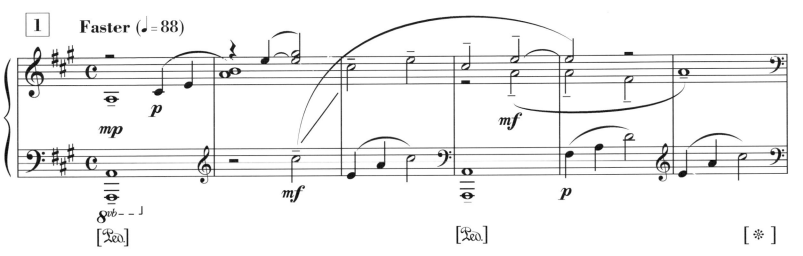

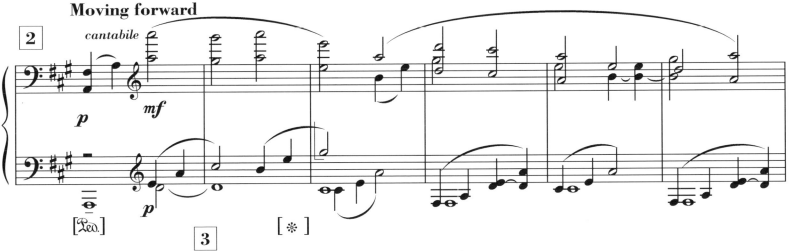

© 1945 by The Aaron Copland Fund For Music, Inc.
Copyright Renewed.
This arrangement © 2007 by The Aaron Copland Fund For Music, Inc.
Boosey & Hawkes, Inc. Sole Licensee.
Copyright for all countries. All Rights Reserved.

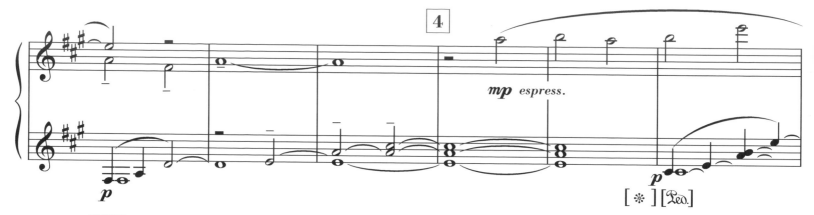

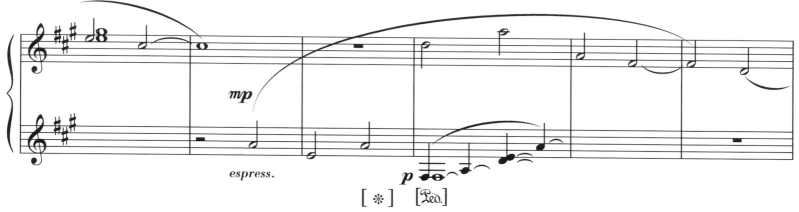

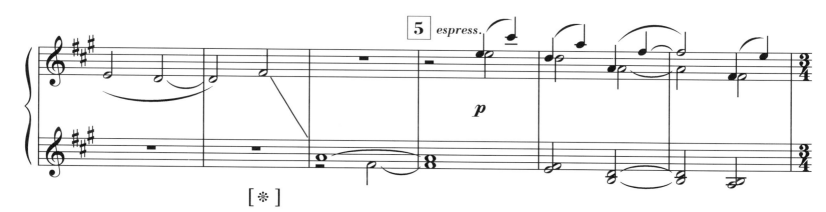

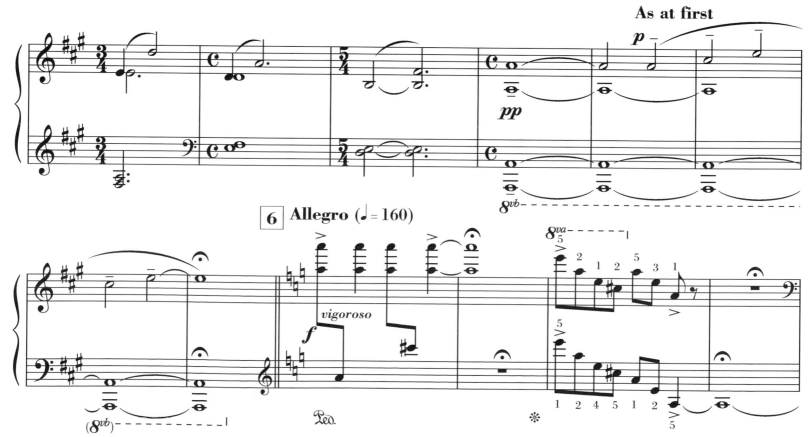

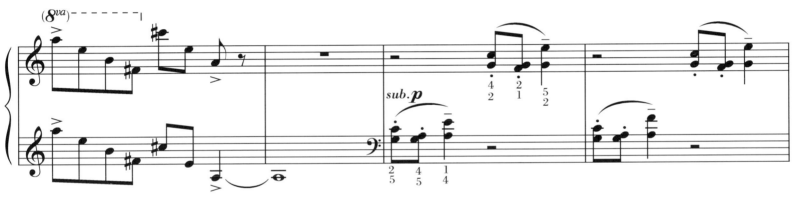

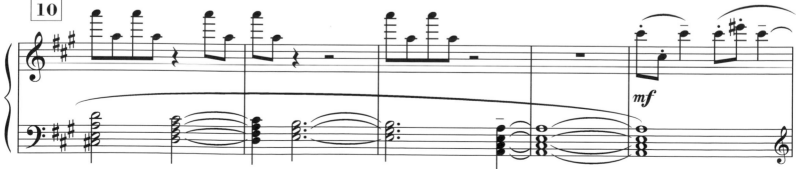

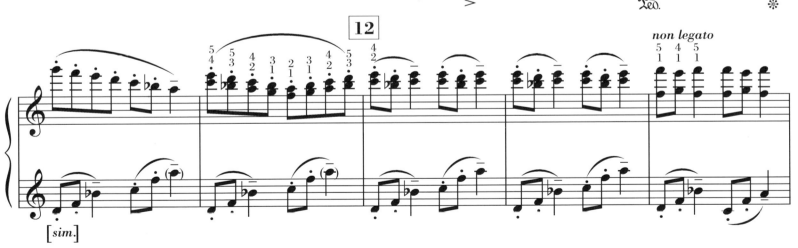

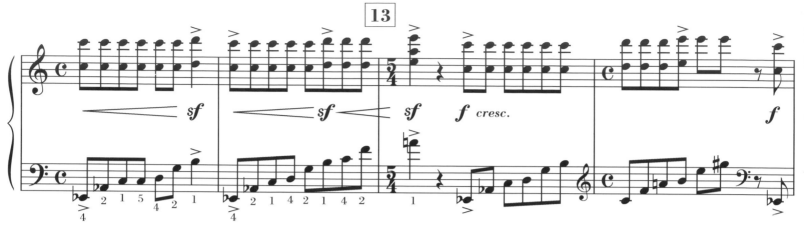

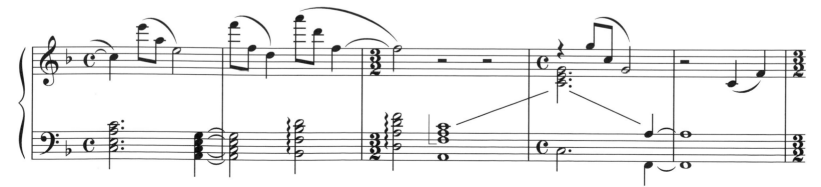

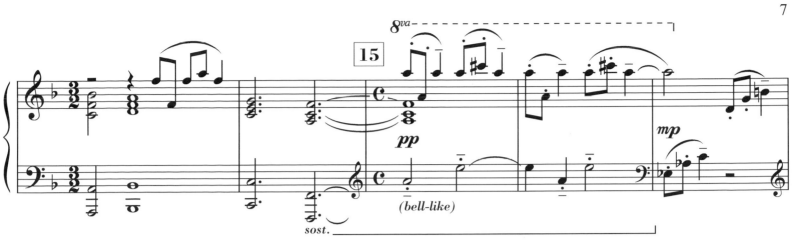

A tempo primo

Slower (♩ = 80)

19 Much slower (♩ = 69)

poco rubato

press forward

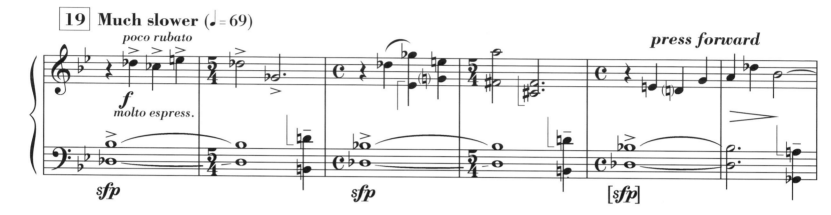

rit.　　*a tempo*

20　　*più accel.*　　*rit.*　　*a tempo*　　*poco accel.*

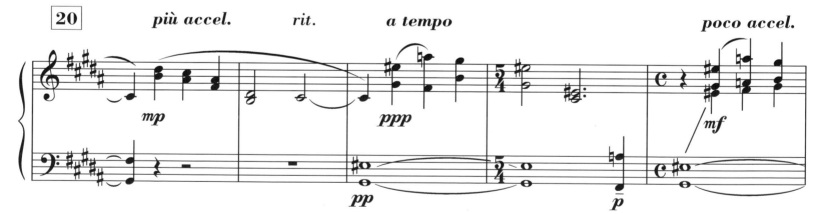

a tempo

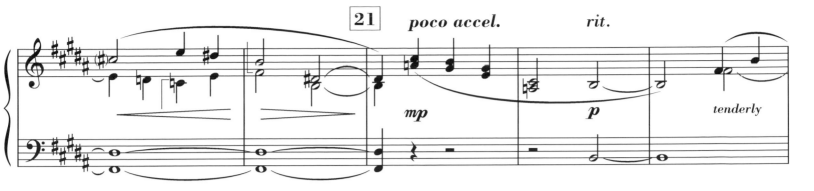

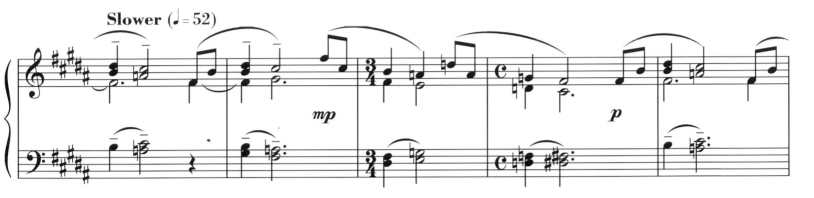

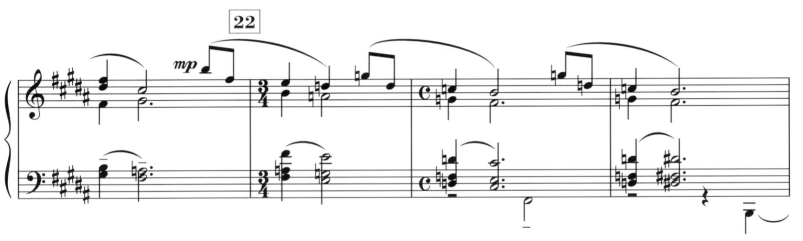

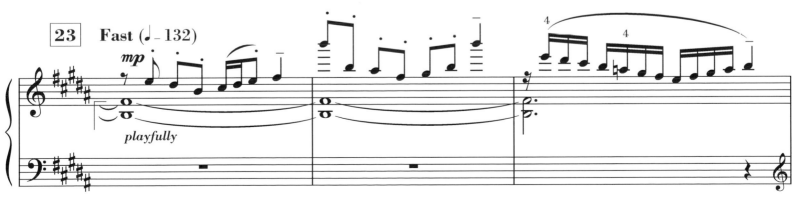

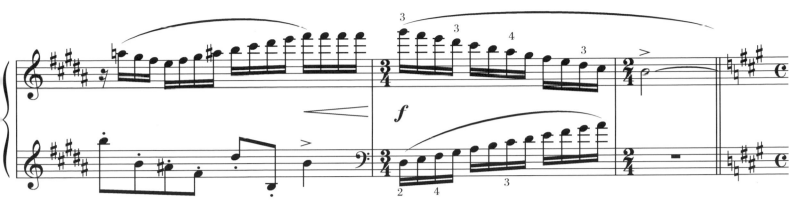

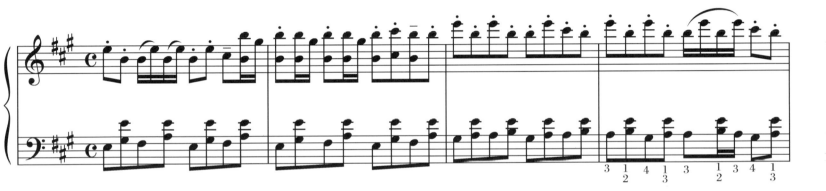

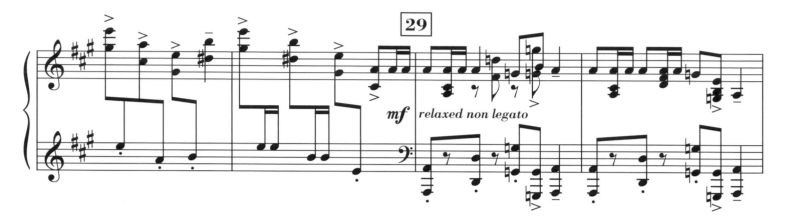

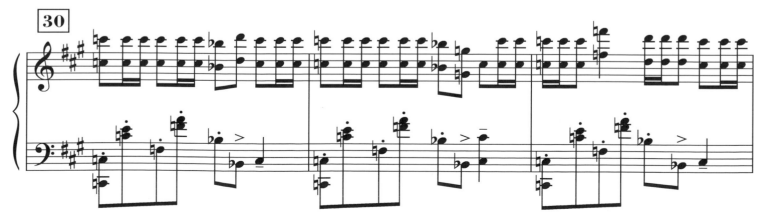

31

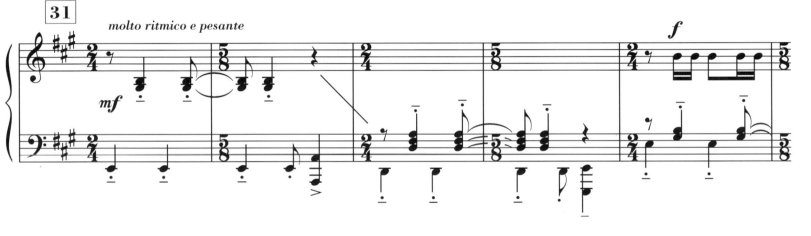

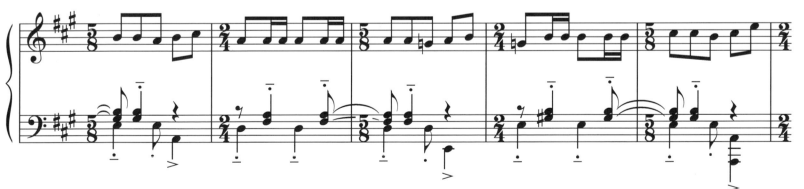

32

14

Molto moderato (♩ = 66)

33

Meno mosso 34

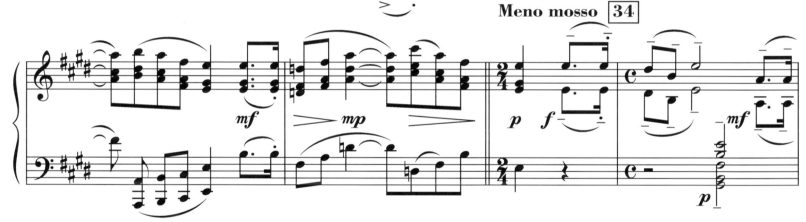

Meno mosso ancora
espress.

rit. 35 Subito allegro (♩ = 160)

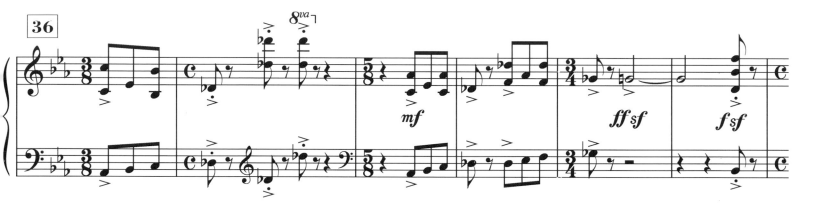

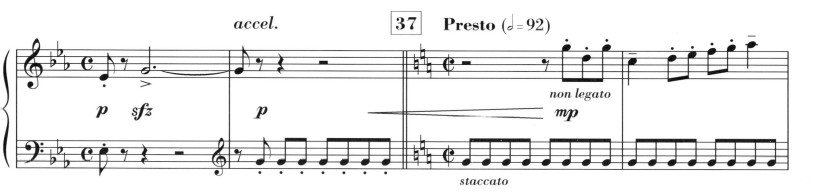

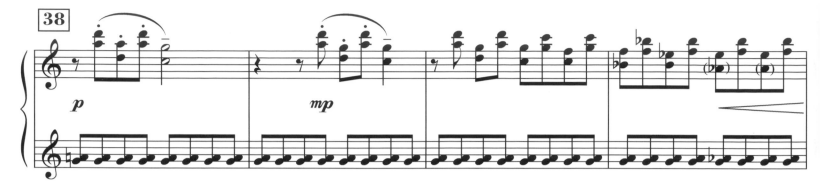

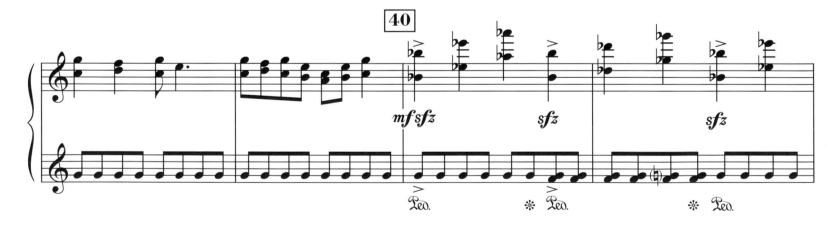

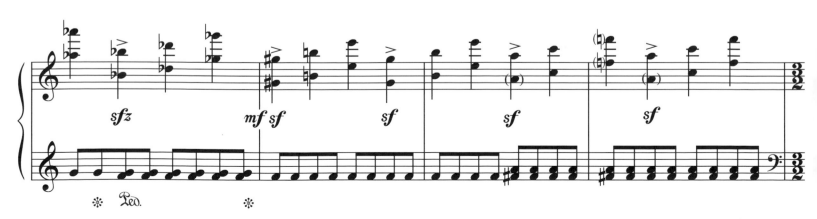

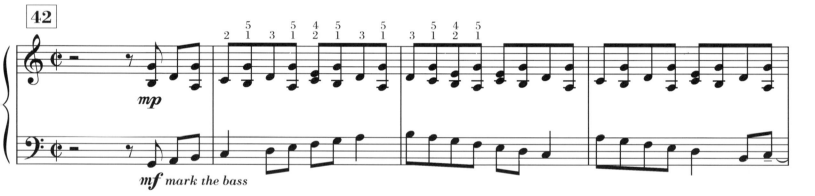

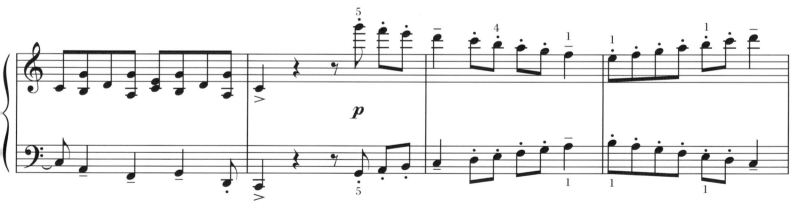

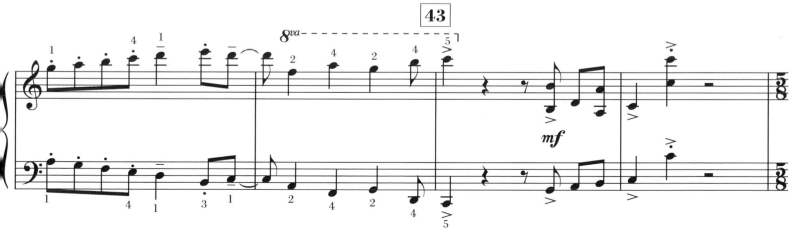

19

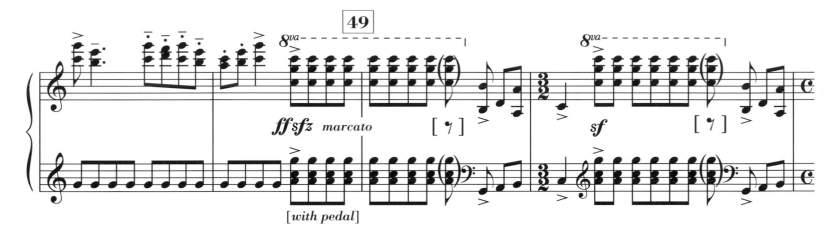

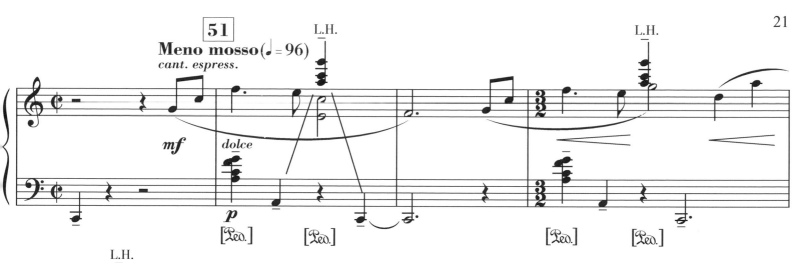

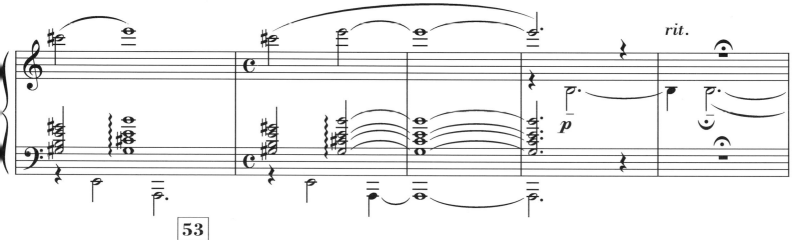

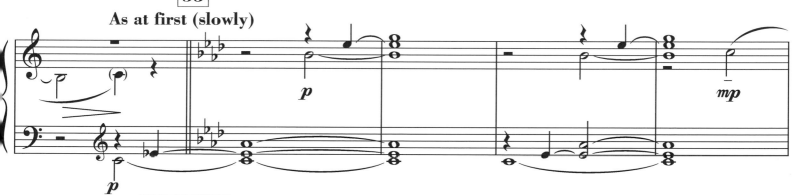

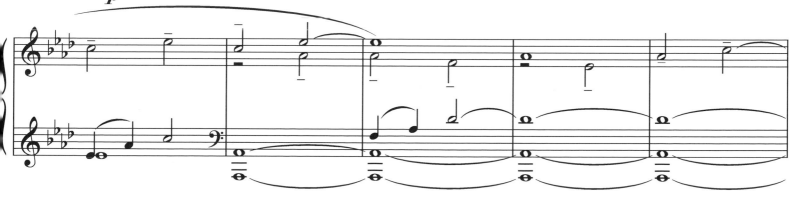

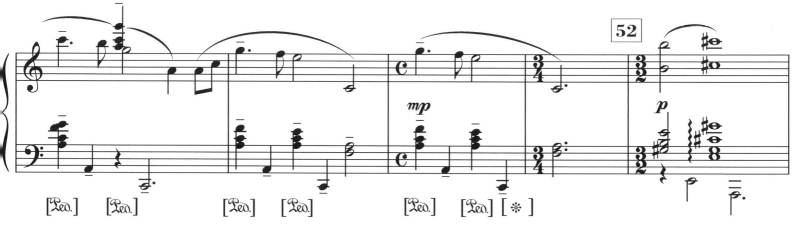

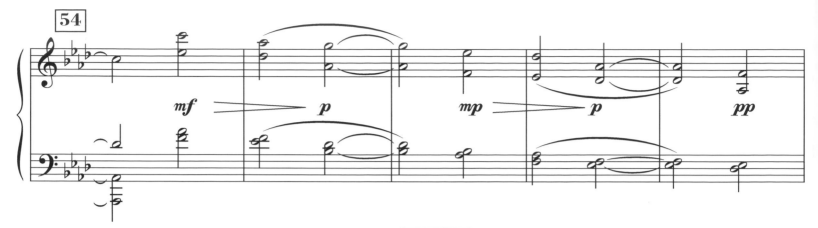

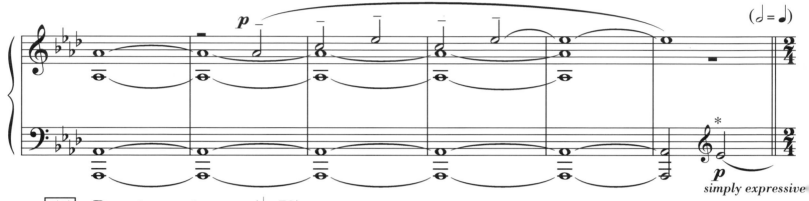

* Shaker Melody: "The gift to be simple"

A trifle faster (♩ = 80)

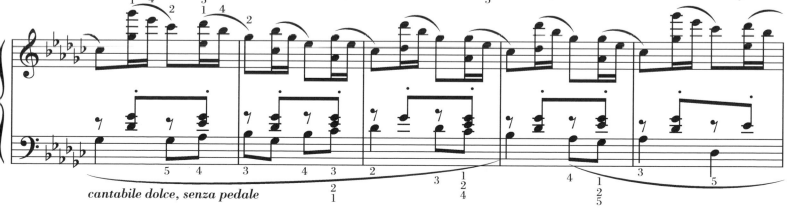

cantabile dolce, senza pedale

move forward

62 **Doppio movimento**
$(\flat = \flat)$

mf

ff vigoroso e marcato (non legato)

63

sf

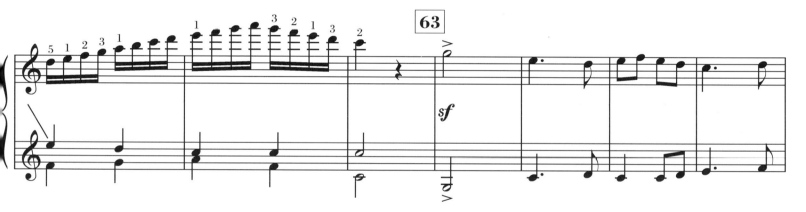

ff

mf

26

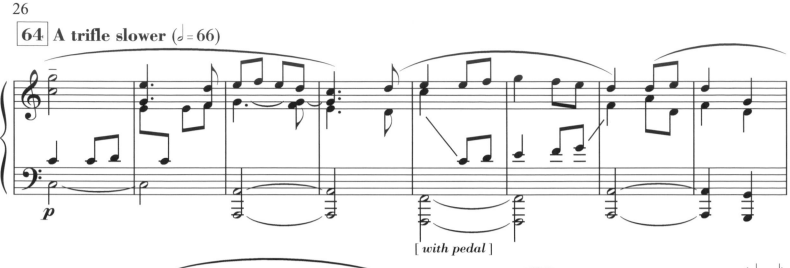

[*with pedal*]

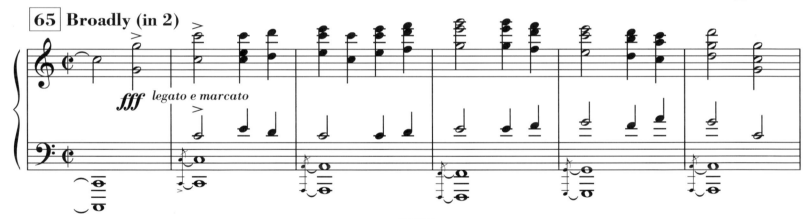

67 **Moderato (like a prayer)** (♩ = 66)

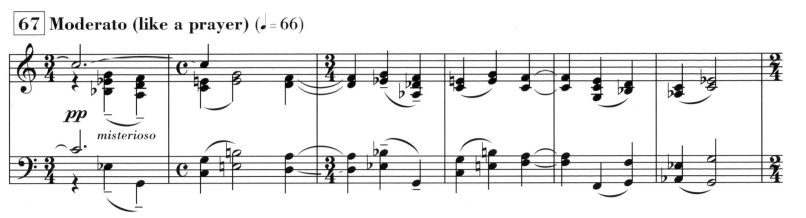

pp

misterioso

poco rit.　　　　　　　　**68** *a tempo*

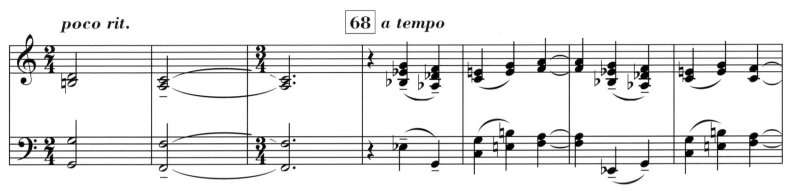

poco rit.　　　　　　　　**69** **Più mosso** (♩ = 88–104)

p dolce

70 **A tempo** (♩ = 66)

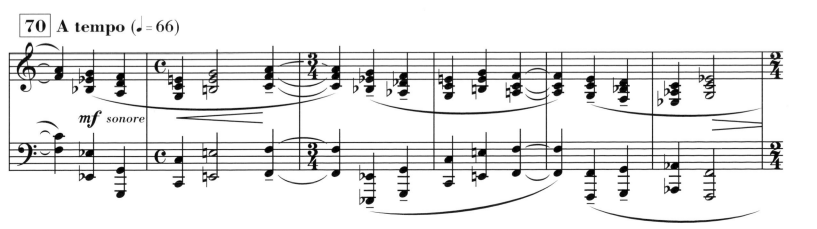

mf sonore

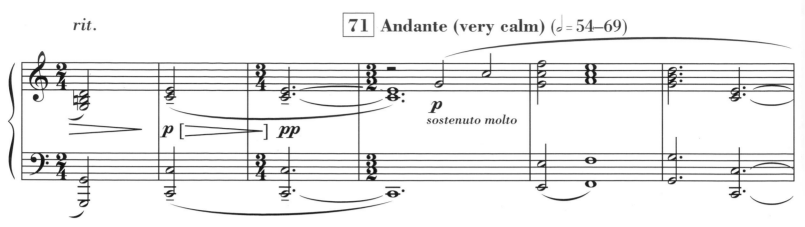

rit. **71** Andante (very calm) (♩=54–69)

p sostenuto molto

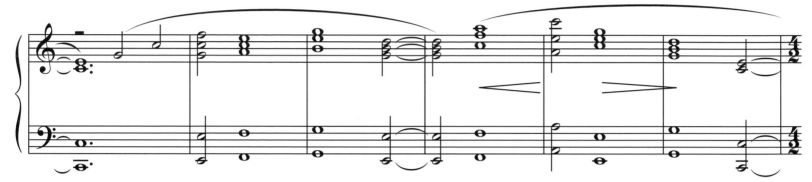

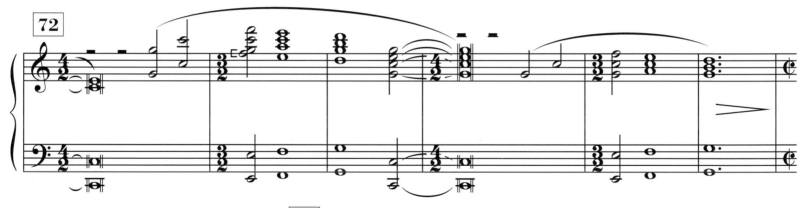

72

73

Slower still [semplice]

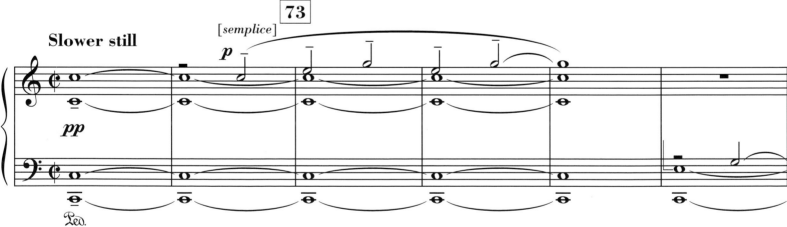

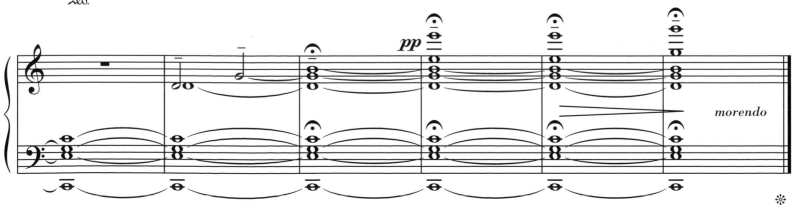

pp *morendo*